Piano Studies / Etudes 2

Celebration Series

PERSPECTIVES®

Library and Archives Canada Cataloguing in Publication

Perspectives [music] : studies = études / Royal Conservatory of Music.

(Celebration series) Previously published under title: The piano odyssey.
To be complete in 10 volumes. ISBN 978-1-55440-175-8 (book 1).
–ISBN 978-1-55440-176-5 (book 2).–ISBN 978-1-55440-177-2 (book 3).
–ISBN 978-1-55440-178-9 (book 4).–ISBN 978-1-55440-179-6 (book 5).
–ISBN 978-1-55440-180-2 (book 6).–ISBN 978-1-55440-181-9 (book 7).
–ISBN 978-1-55440-182-6 (book 8).–ISBN 978-1-55440-183-3 (book 9).
–ISBN 978-1-55440-184-0 (book 10)

1. Piano–Studies and exercises. I. Royal Conservatory of Music II. Title. III. Series

MT222.P46 2008 786.2 C2007-906502-3

17 16 15 14 13 12 11 10 09 08 1 2 3 4 5 6 7 8 9 10

Celebration Series Perspectives®

The Royal Conservatory of Music is pleased to present *Celebration Series Perspectives®*, the fourth edition of this renowned piano series. The *Celebration Series®* was first published in 1987 to international acclaim. Subsequent editions have built on this success: *Celebration Series®, The Piano Odyssey®* (2001) in particular tapped into the wealth of new repertoire available at the dawn of the new millennium, and took into account the changing interests and needs of teachers. This achievement was recognized when The Frederick Harris Music Co., Limited received the 2007 MTNA-Frances Clark Keyboard Pedagogy Award for the *Celebration Series®*.

Celebration Series Perspectives® is breathtaking in its scope, presenting a kaleidoscopic overview of keyboard music from the last four centuries. The graded *Piano Repertoire* books encompass early elementary to early intermediate levels (Preparatory to 4); intermediate to late intermediate levels (5 to 7); and early advanced to advanced levels (8 to 10). The repertoire comprises a carefully selected grouping of pieces from the Baroque, Classical, Romantic, 20th-, and 21st-century style periods. *Piano Studies / Etudes* books present compositions especially suited for building the technique and musicality relevant to the repertoire of each level. *Student Workbooks* and the corresponding *Answer Book* (Preparatory to 8), as well as the outstanding recordings of the entire series, are available to assist in the study and enjoyment of the music. In addition, the comprehensive *Handbook for Teachers* is an invaluable pedagogical resource.

A Note on Editing and Performance Practice

Most Baroque and early Classical composers wrote few dynamics, articulation, or other performance indications in their scores. Interpretation was left up to the performer, with the expectation that the performance practice was understood. Even into the 19th century, composers' scores could vary from copy to copy or edition to edition. The editors of *Celebration Series Perspectives®* have consulted original sources wherever possible and have kept editorial additions to a minimum.

Metronome markings include a range to assist the student and teacher in arriving at a suitable tempo for each piece. Editorial markings, including fingering and the execution of ornaments, are intended to be helpful rather than definitive.

This edition follows the policy that the bar line cancels accidentals. In accordance with current practice, cautionary accidentals are added only in cases of possible ambiguity.

Students and teachers should refer to the companion guides—the *Student Workbooks* and the *Handbook for Teachers*—for further discussion of style and pedagogical elements. For examination requirements of The Royal Conservatory of Music and the National Music Certificate Program, please refer to the *Piano Syllabus, 2008 Edition*.

Dr. Trish Sauerbrei
Editor-in-Chief

Contents

Study / Etude no. 1

Asteroids

Christopher Norton
(b. 1953)

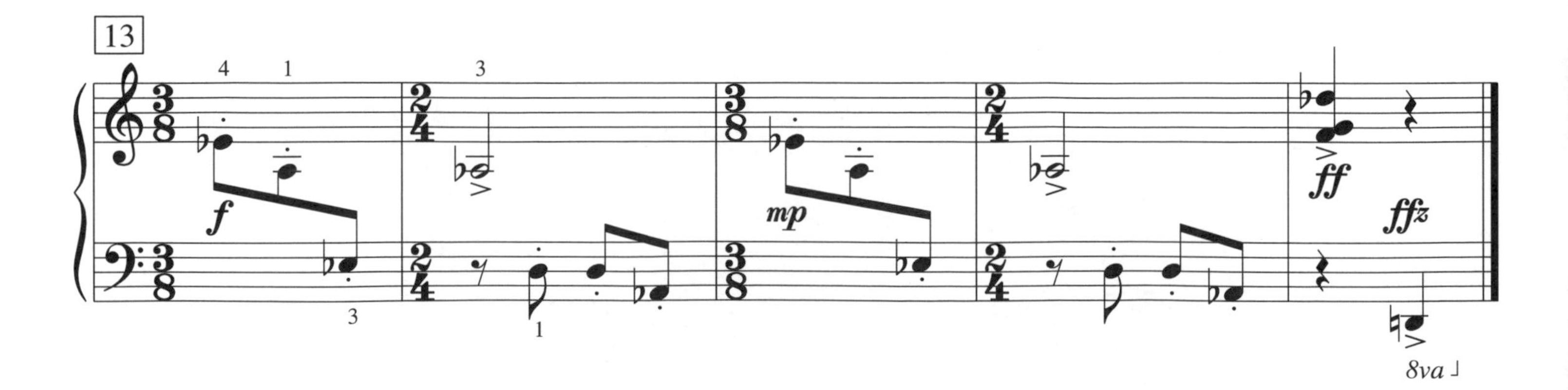

Source: *The Final Frontier*

Study / Etude no. 2

Scherzo

op. 39, no. 12

Dmitri Kabalevsky
(1904–1987)

Vivo, giocoso ♩ **= 108 – 116**

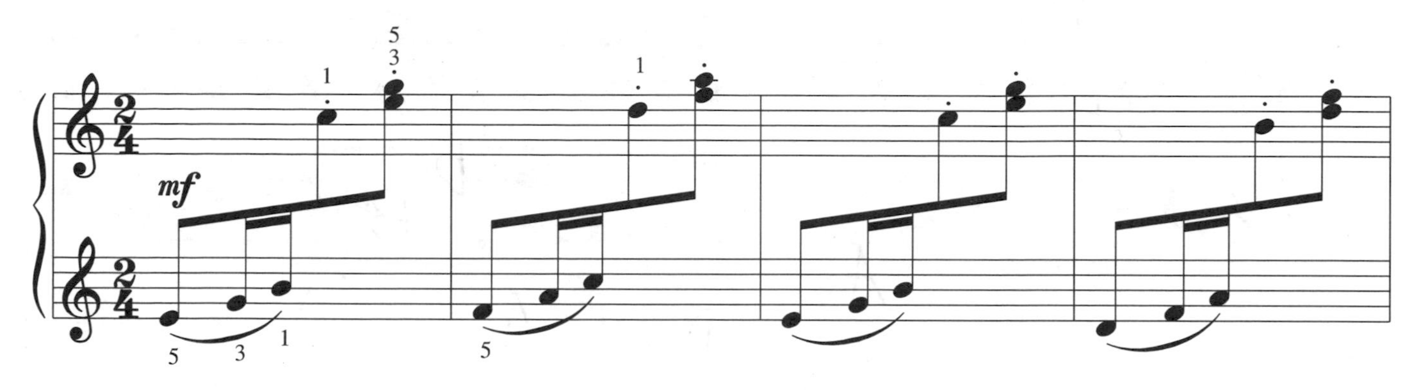

Source: *24 Little Pieces*, op. 39 (1944)

Study / Etude no. 3

Etude in D Minor

op. 82, no. 65

Cornelius Gurlitt
(1820–1901)

Source: *Die ersten Schritte des jungen Klavierspielers,* op. 82

Study / Etude no. 4

Baseball Practice

Linda Niamath
(b. 1939)

Energetically ♩ = 144 – 160

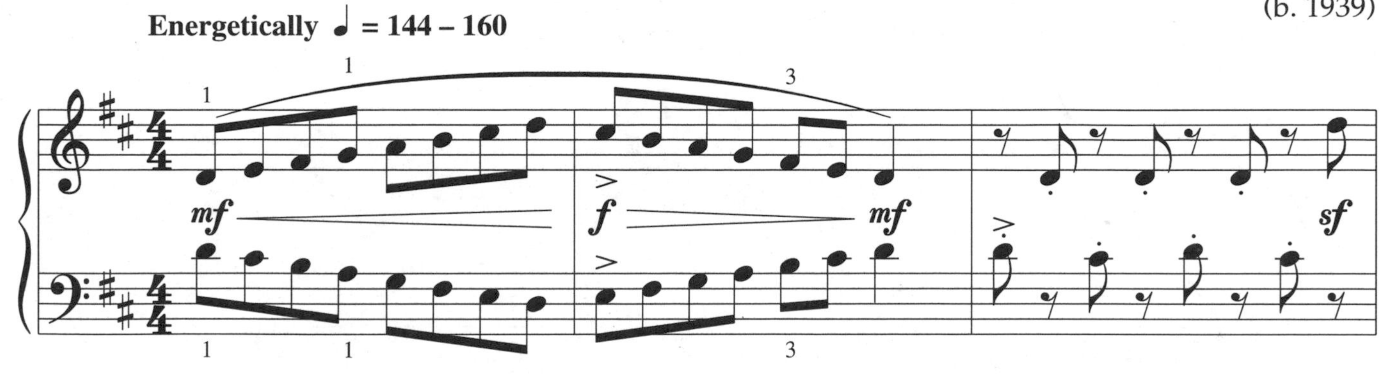

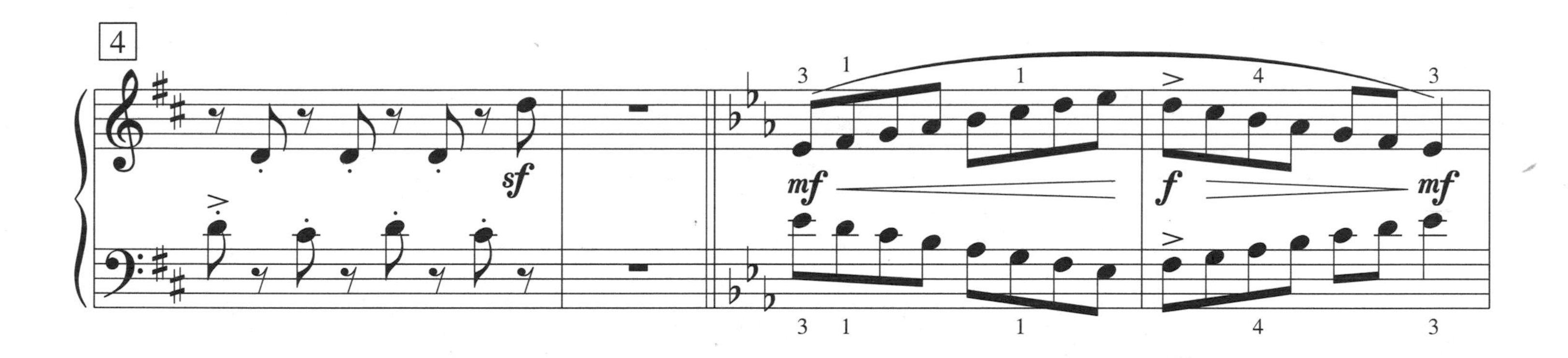

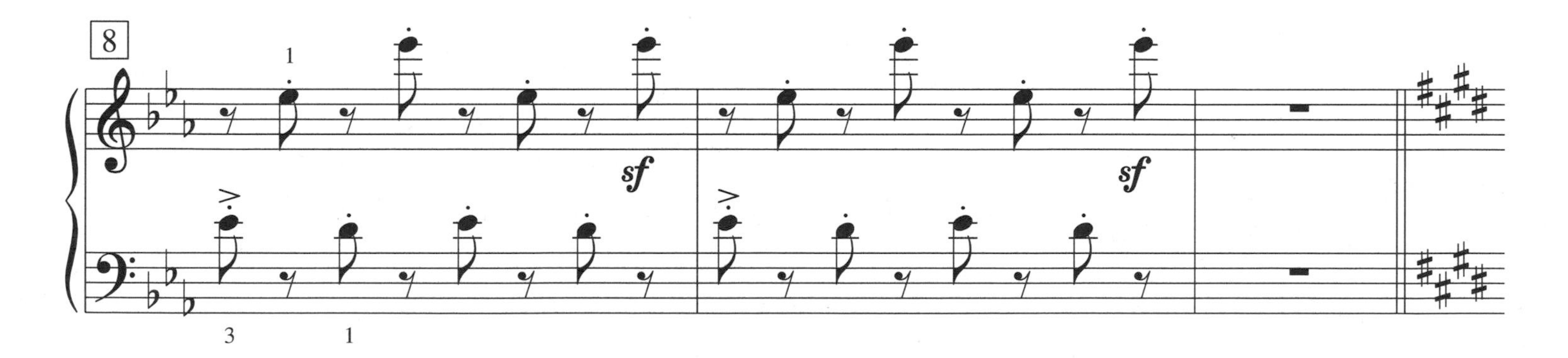

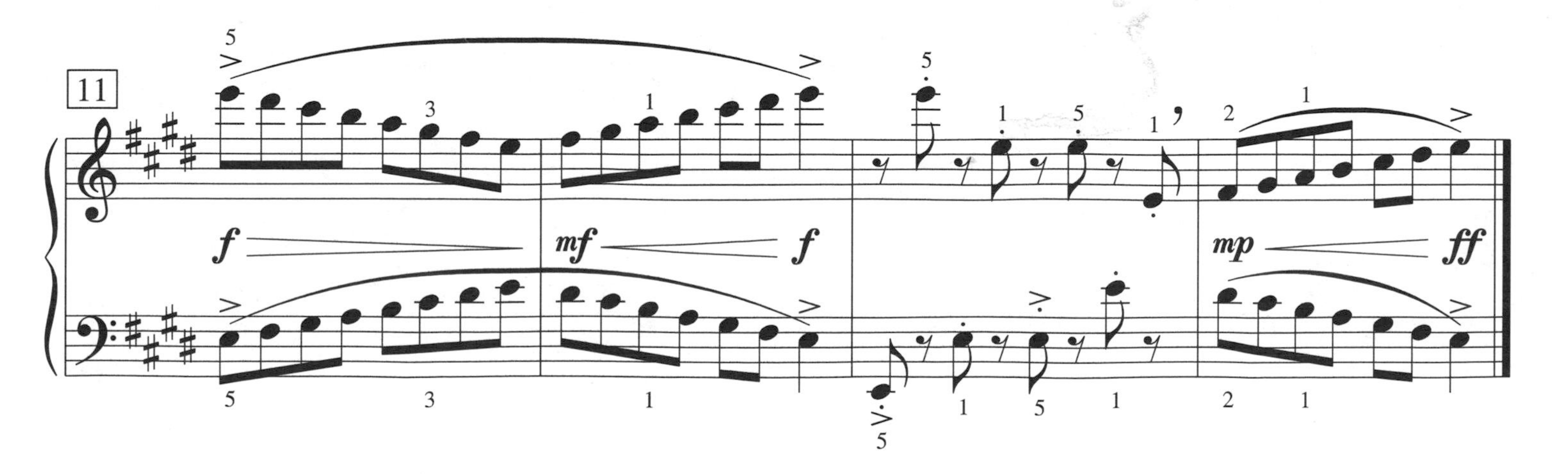

Source: *All Year Round*

Study / Etude no. 5

Kangaroos

Veronika Krausas
(b. 1963)

Source: *The Bestiary*

Study / Etude no. 6

Crocodile Teeth

Nancy Telfer
(b. 1950)

Not too quickly ♩ **= 96 – 104**

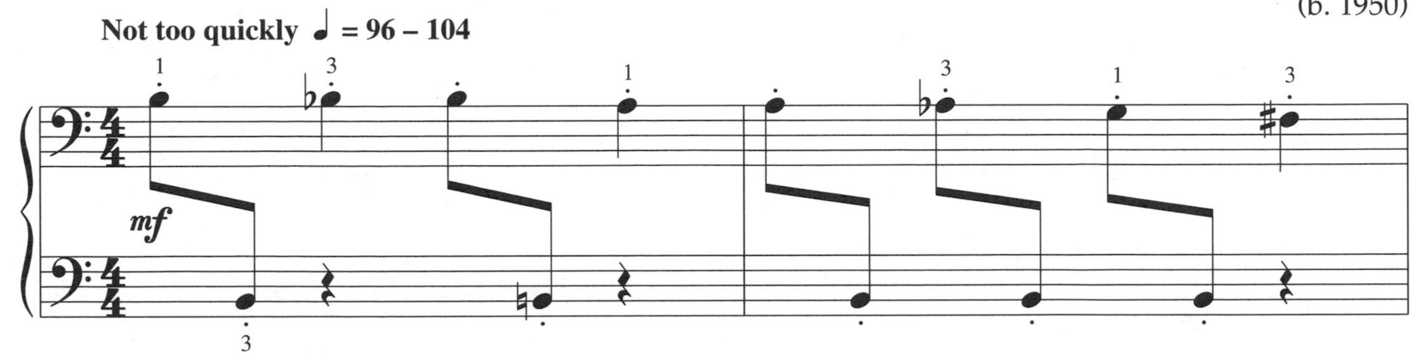

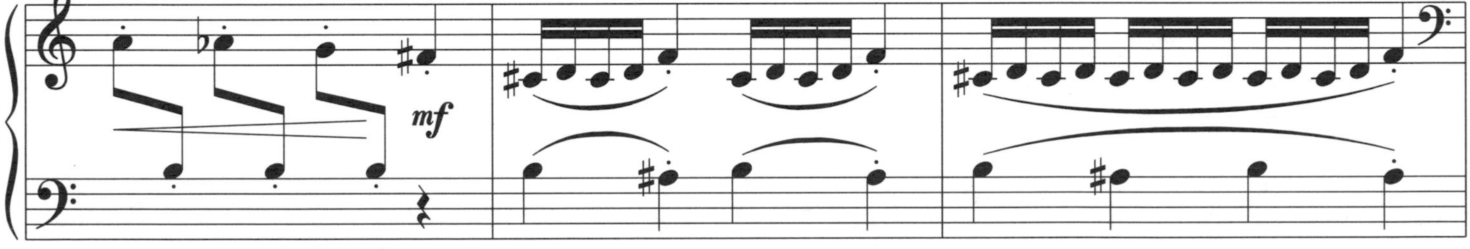

Source: *I'm Not Scared*

Study / Etude no. 7

Study in F Major

op. 190, no. 27

Christian Louis Heinrich Köhler
(1820–1886)

Source: *Die allerleichtesten Übungsstücke für den Clavierunterricht*, op. 190 (Liepzig, *ca* 1871)

Study / Etude no. 8

Little Lopsided Waltz

Source: *Clowning Around*

Study / Etude no. 9

Crazy Comics

Christine Donkin
(b. 1976)

With pizzazz ♩ = 120 – 132

Source: *Comics & Card Tricks*

Study / Etude no. 10

Study in C Major

op. 261, no. 3

Carl Czerny
(1791–1857)

Allegro ♪ **= 144 – 160**

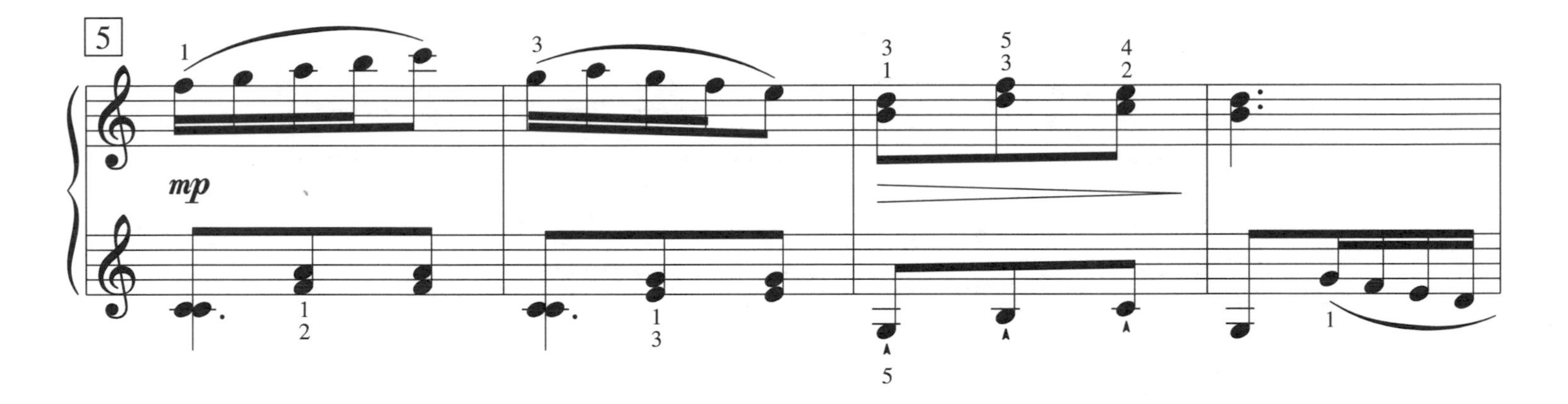

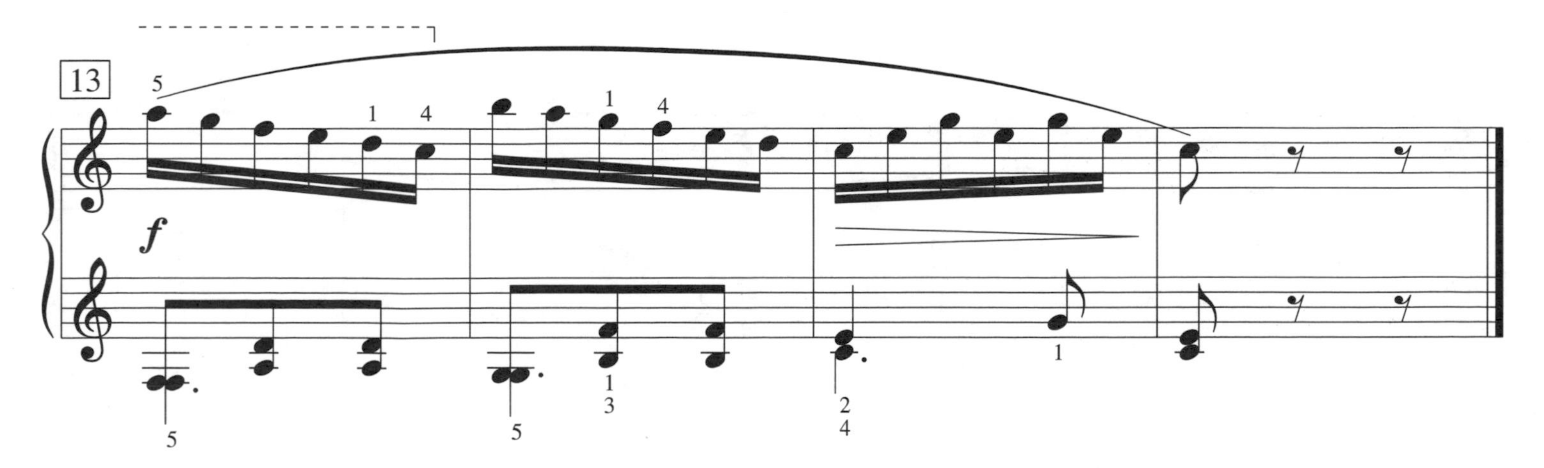

Source: *125 Passagen-übungen*, op. 261

Study / Etude no. 11

Study in A Minor

Pál Kadosa
(1903–1983)

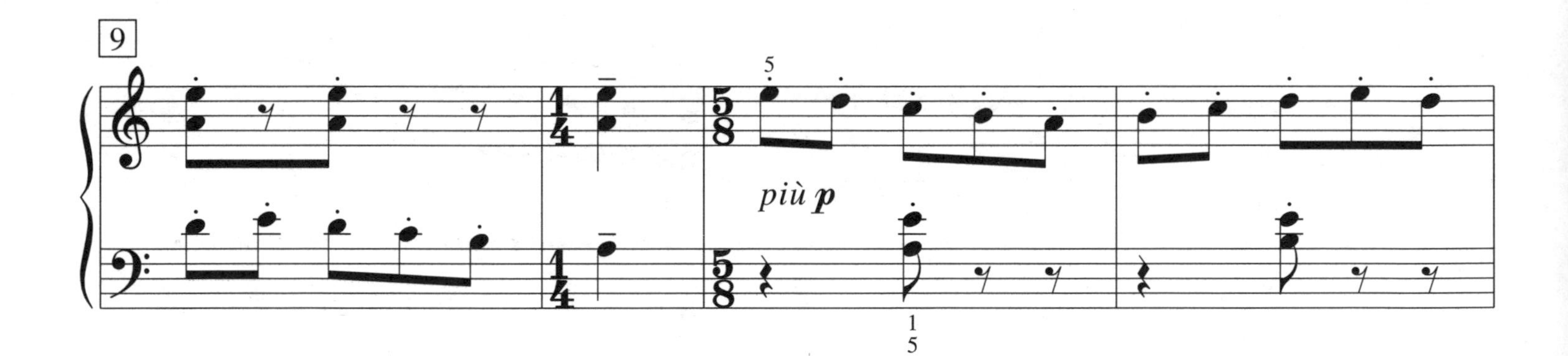

Source: *Fourteen Little Pieces*, in vol. 1 of *55 Small Piano Pieces*

Study / Etude no. 12

The Wind

Chee-Hwa Tan
(b. 1965)

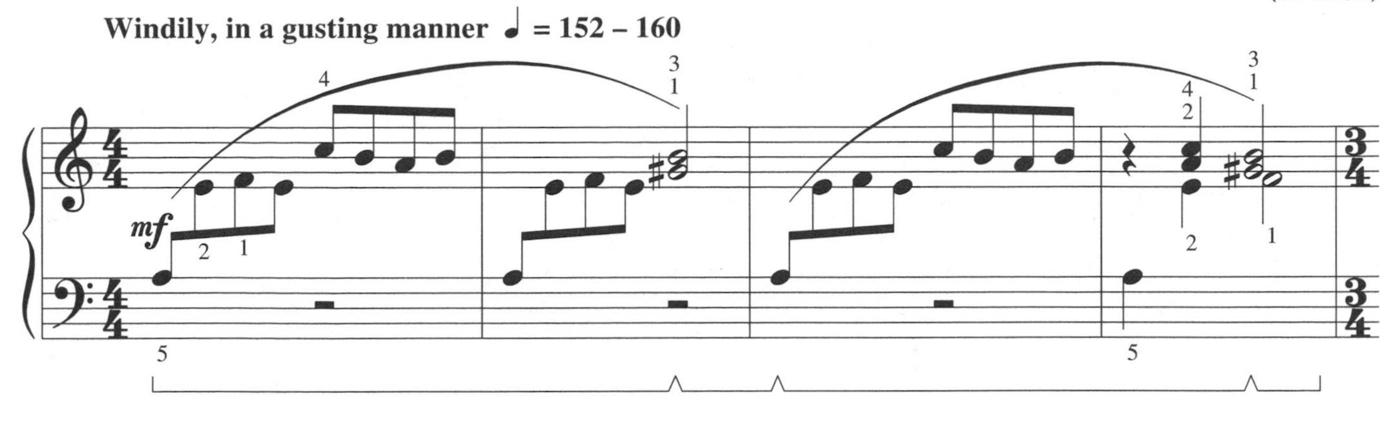

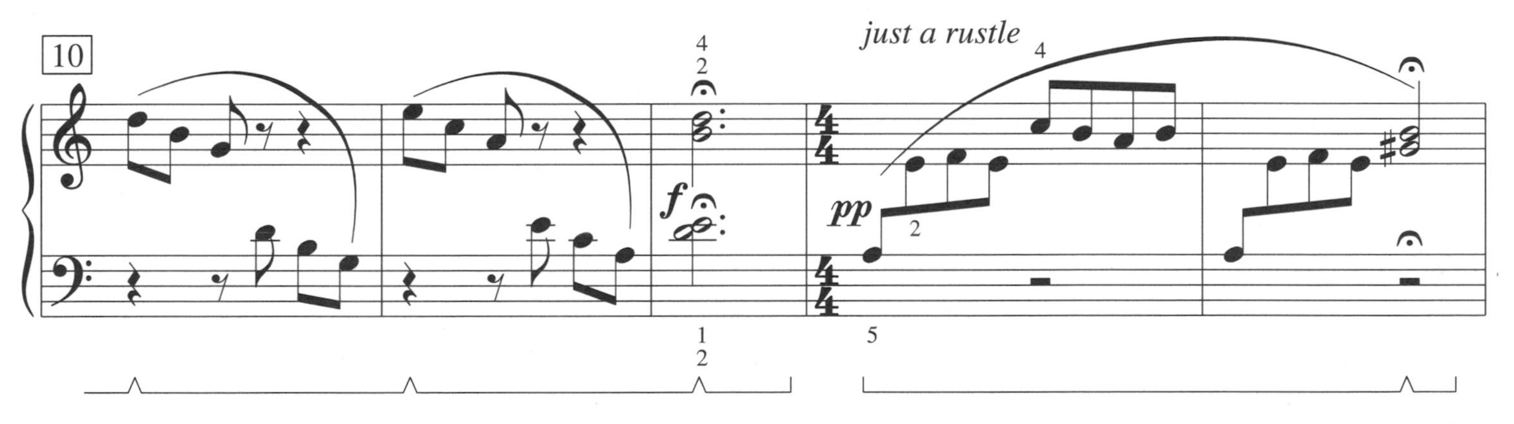

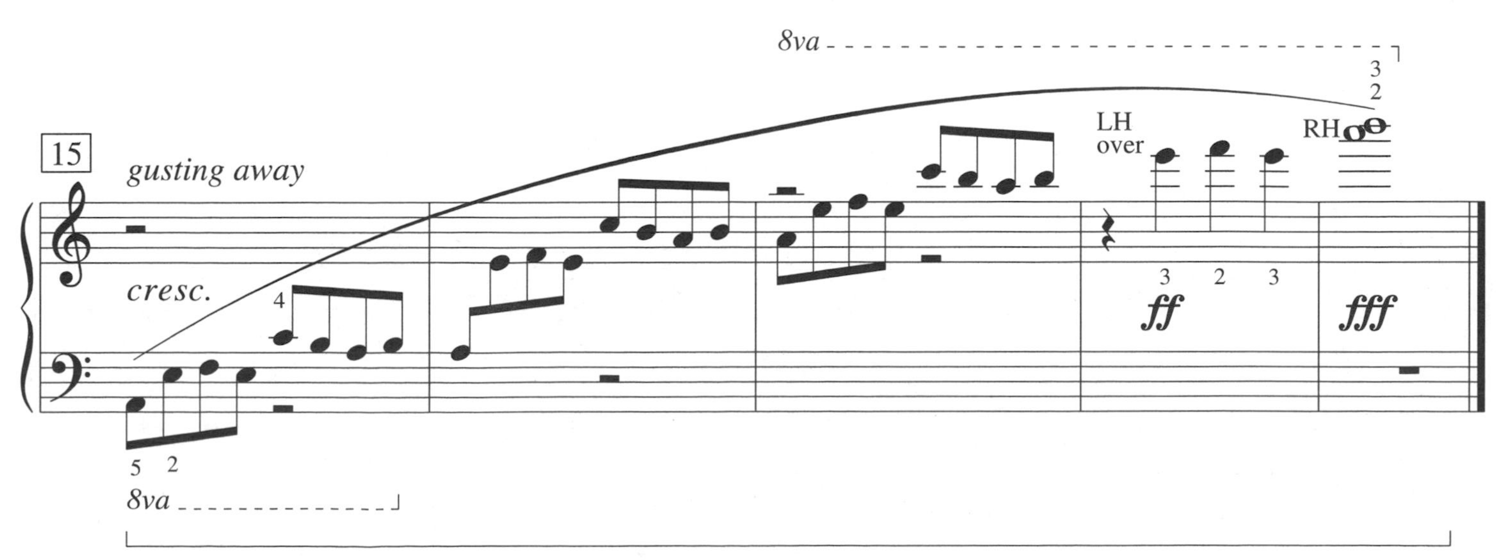

Source: *A Child's Garden of Verses*

Study / Etude no. 13

Celebration

Linda Niamath
(b. 1939)

Source: *All Year Round*